START FINISHING
FIELD GUIDE

Productive Flourishing
Portland, OR 97206

Published 2022

Book and cover design by Stauber Brand Studio, https://stauberbrandstudio.com
Illustrations by Cristina Kramp, https://www.cristinakramp.com
Source cover design by Rachael Murray, courtesy of Sounds True Inc.

ISBN Print 979-8-9854416-0-4
ISBN Ebook 979-8-9854416-1-1

Library of Congress Control Number: 2022901593

START
FINISHING
FIELD GUIDE

CHARLIE GILKEY

productive
FLOURISHING

CONTENTS

INTRODUCTION

One of my top goals for *Start Finishing* was that it'd be a resource that lived on people's shelves after they read it. I hoped it'd be a highlighted, dog-eared, and well-used and -loved book that'd help people in different phases of their journey with their best work, in different projects, and in different seasons of their lives.

What many readers have told me is that not only did that happen, but they also wanted a place to answer the prompts and reflect on the questions I pose in the book. Chapters 4–6, especially, have a lot of project- or time-specific questions.

We've designed this workbook in the hope that it helps you find a home for the prompts, reflections, and action steps that *Start Finishing* guides you through. Much like *Start Finishing*, we want you to write in this book, dog-ear it, highlight, and make it your own, but, unlike *Start Finishing*, we do not want this to sit on your shelf. We want it to sit on your desk while you're working on a project that matters. When you finish the project, part of your CAT work (chapter 10) might be recycling, burning, or storing it away in a project box.

Start Finishing is for life; this workbook is for a project.

Not only is each project different, but each project meets you in time in a different way. What was a challenge during last quarter's project may not be a challenge for this quarter's project. The key player on your success pack for the last project may not be on your success pack at all for this one. As you create and finish your best work, you create yourself and the nexus of possibilities that's in front of you.

I say all of this to give you permission to only hang onto this workbook as long as it serves you and to use it however it serves you. Much like *Start Finishing*, there will be some sections that will challenge or constructively frustrate you; our goal with these is to get you to engage with the dragons, uncertainty, head trash, and constraints directly rather than letting their unhelpful murkiness catalyze a thrash crash. These sections may not be comfortable, but they're still there to help you do your best work.

If there's a section that doesn't serve you, skip it.

If there's a question that strikes you in a dissonant way, ignore it or rewrite it in a way that works for you.

If something appears to present a "one right way" that doesn't work for you, consider how the principle or insight might be relevant to you but applied a different way. (It's exceedingly rare for there to only be one right way.)

One last thing: you have what you need to start finishing your best work and start building the future you want to live in. Right now. Yes, you.

The book and this workbook just remind you of your potential, tap into it, and channel it towards what matters most.

Commit to the work (aka yourself), build your success pack, stick with it, and run your victory lap. You've got this.

Charlie Gilkey
January 2022
Portland, Oregon

PS: A book doesn't happen without a dedicated success pack to see it through (see chapter 4 for how to create your own). As is usual for all Productive Flourishing projects, everyone here at PF has played a role in getting this field guide finished and in your hands.

That said, special shoutouts are owed to Maghan Haggerty and Steve Arensberg, both of whom championed for, significantly contributed to, and pushed the project through the successive red zones on its way to done. Without Steve and Maghan, this field guide would not exist.

Thanks to Joy Panos Stauber of Stauber Brand Studio for turning our rough ideas and raw text into polished, accessible designs and Cristina Kramp for lending her unique artistry to the project with her whimsical chapter images (and a few others).

Thanks to Sounds True for being the wonderful publishing partner that gave us the green light to create this companion work alongside *Start Finishing*.

Last, but definitely not least, thanks to all the *Start Finishing* readers, discussion group leaders, and facilitators who've nudged us for this field guide — may it serve you and those you're catalyzing well.

PART 1

CLEARING THE DECKS FOR
YOUR BEST WORK

🍃 Day _someday_   Date _TODAY_

TODAY'S PROJECTS
What will you focus on?

	Project	Due Date
1		
2		
3		
4		
5		

SCHEDULED EVENTS
What is planned for today?

Time	Event

SUPPORTING TASKS
What's needed for your projects?

- [ ]
- [ ]
- [ ]
- [ ]
- [ ]
- [ ]

EMERGENT TASKS
What's popped up?

- [ ]
- [ ]
- [ ]
- [ ]
- [ ]
- [ ]

TODAY'S SCHEDULE
When will you do your tasks?

:00
:30
:00
:30
:00
:30
:00
:30
:00
:30
:00
:30
:00
:30
:00
:30
:00
:30
:00
:30
:00
:30
:00
:30
:00
:30
:00
:30
:00
:30

someday can be Today

"SOMEDAY"
CAN BE TODAY

Buried under busywork, responsibility, distraction, and fatigue sit the difference-making and joy-producing ideas, waiting for someday. The trouble is "someday" never comes on its own. But you can decide that today is the day you stop waiting and start finishing.

 WE DON'T DO IDEAS; WE DO PROJECTS

Ideas are formless. In order to take action and make progress you'll need to turn your ideas into projects.

Project = anything that takes time, energy, and attention to complete

Yes, by this definition pretty much everything can be considered a project. As overwhelming as that might be, it also provides clarity to what is and is not getting our limited time, energy, and attention. To get to the place our soul longs to be, we're going to have to convert our ideas into doable projects at the same time that we're going to have to get real about all the projects we are doing.

Where are you spending your time, energy, and attention?

_____

_____

_____

_____

_____

_____

_____

_____

Many people end up with their days filled with projects they aren't counting, but what does count to them are counted projects that aren't getting done.

◉ WE THRIVE BY DOING OUR BEST WORK

We all have work that calls to us. The work that goes beyond simply doing but leaves us fulfilled and leads to our *flourishing*.

Best work = the work that leads to our thriving

The truth about best work:

Your best work can be sacred. It can be what makes you come alive. It can be joyful.

Only you can do your best work. Only you have the set of experiences, expertise, skills, and perspectives to do it.

Your best work serves you *and* others. There's no either/or perspective about who's being served by the work. It's all.

Your best work requires *really* showing up. Your best work will always be on the edge of your capabilities and comfort levels.

Your best work is easily displaced by other stuff. There's always something to do that's easier, more urgent, less risky, or more likely to please others.

Your best work is more than just your "job." Your best work may not be translatable to work you would do in a conventional day job.

What does best work mean to you? What past projects fall into this category?

_____

_____

_____

_____

_____

PROJECTS ARE MIRRORS AND BRIDGES

Mirrors

Projects reflect back to us what's really going on in our inner and outer worlds.

Bridges

Projects are the connections between where we are and where our souls want to be.

What have your past best-work projects shown you about yourself?

_____

_____

_____

_____

_____

What bridges did they create?

_____

_____

_____

_____

_____

HOW TO USE THIS FIELD GUIDE

Similar to *Start Finishing*, this field guide is organized into three distinct parts that roughly track what you'll need to do to go from idea to done.

Part 1:
Clearing the Decks for Your Best Work

Part 2:
Planning Your Project

Part 3:
Working the Plan

We've also added a bonus chapter to help you if your project gets stuck (as projects tend to do).

You'll focus on one quarter-sized project throughout this book.
Use this one project to get comfortable with the methodology and then apply what you learn to all your future projects.

Pace yourself. This book is not meant to be finished in one sitting. Take time to go through each exercise. Keep this guide with you as you plan, execute, and complete your one project.

This Field Guide is packed full of exercises. These will walk you through the journey of finishing step-by-step.

The journey to finishing can be a messy one. Use a pencil and embrace the mistakes you're going to make.

You'll find more information and worksheets on the topic on the Resources page (link in the back of the book).

The best resource of all is ***Start Finishing***. Read it side by side with this field guide for more depth, examples, and background.

GO FROM IDEA TO DONE

Chapter 2   Learn what's getting between you and your best work.

Chapter 3   Pick the one best-work idea you'll move to done.

Chapter 4   Convert that idea into a project.

Chapter 5   Break down that project into manageable parts.

Chapter 6   Create a project roadmap that leverages your skills and resources.

Chapter 7   Learn to anticipate challenges and create strategies to keep moving forward.

Chapter 8   Integrate the actionable steps of your project into your calendar.

Chapter 9   Learn how to keep momentum going day-to-day.

Chapter 10   Learn what to do once you've crossed the finish line.

Bonus chapter Learn how to navigate projects that have gotten stuck.

Then you'll pick a new project and do it all over again.

It's time to start finishing.

THE AIR SANDWICH

VISION
MISSION
PURPOSE

BIG GOALS

competing priorities
head trash
no realistic plan
too few resources
poor team alignment

DAY-TO-DAY REALITY

The air sandwich shows the five challenges that create the gap between your big picture and your day-to-day reality.

GETTING TO
YOUR BEST WORK

Your best work is the thing you *have* to do, and often what the world *needs* you to do. So it's more than just a matter of finding the motivation or drive to do your best work — you have to address the parts of your life that are keeping you from that doing.

THE AIR SANDWICH

VISION
MISSION
PURPOSE

BIG GOALS

competing priorities
head trash
no realistic plan
too few resources
poor team alignment

DAY-TO-DAY REALITY

THE FIVE CHALLENGES

There are five different challenges that combine to keep us from spending our days working on what matters most.

Competing Priorities

Often the result of us not acknowledging our priorities and not seeing how our goals and plans end up at odds. It's difficult to make progress on any one goal when your attention is diverted to other things.

Head Trash

The beliefs holding us back from making progress on our goals. It's the adult version of the monster under the bed; its power over us relies upon it remaining in the darkness.

No Realistic Plan

Some folks have a plan, but it's not realistic. Others don't have a plan at all. Others confuse an aspiration or idea for a plan and aren't getting anywhere.

Too Few Resources

We let what we don't have keep us from creating what we *can* have, instead of considering how we can either use what we do have or obtain the resources we need.

Poor Team Alignment

Many of us have poor team alignment not because the people on our team are in conflict but because we're not communicating to our team what we want, need, and dream to be.

⬤ THE FIVE KEYS TO OVERCOMING THE AIR SANDWICH

If the air sandwich shows us which doors need to be unlocked, we have five keys that can unlock any of these doors. Read through the descriptions below and determine how often you have applied these keys in the past.

	RARELY				OFTEN
	1	2	3	4	5
Intention Plans and goals are intentions about the way you will (and won't) use your time, as well as what is and isn't important to you.	☐	☐	☐	☐	☐
Awareness Awareness is required to know what your best work is and to notice how your emotions and presence shift when you're doing your best work.	☐	☐	☐	☐	☐
Boundaries Boundaries create space for you to get what you want. Positive boundaries create space for something and negative boundaries create space from something.	☐	☐	☐	☐	☐
Courage Courage is more important than talent when finishing what matters most, for courageous action can build talent, but fear keeps us stuck in yesterday.	☐	☐	☐	☐	☐
Discipline Discipline is channeling your energy into purposeful, constructive action; your habits are discipline made automatic.	☐	☐	☐	☐	☐

The keys are both the obstacle and the way to your best work, depending on what you choose to practice.

USING THE FIVE KEYS TO ADDRESS THE FIVE CHALLENGES

Some keys are more effective at overcoming certain challenges than others. To see what challenge(s) might give you particular trouble, use your self-appraisal scores on the five keys to generate a score for each of the five challenges below. The challenges with the lowest scores need more attention.

CHALLENGE	ASSOCIATED KEYS	RATING	FINAL SCORE
Align competing priorities	Awareness		
	Boundaries		
	Discipline		
Take out your head trash	Awareness		
	Courage		
	Discipline		
Remove the no from no realistic plan	Awareness		
	Discipline		
	Intention		
Overcome too few resources	Awareness		
	Courage		
	Discipline		
Get your team to work with and for you	Awareness		
	Boundaries		
	Courage		

Based on these scores, which of the five challenges are most likely to trip you up? Do these scores align with your past experience? What strategies might you employ to help face those challenges on your next project? Which keys do you most need to practice?

⊕ See chapter 2 of *Start Finishing* for a rough guide on using the different keys to overcome each of the five challenges.

◉ WHICH KEYS NEED MORE (OR LESS) PRACTICE?

The five keys are practiced behaviors that we can over- or undercultivate. Either cultivation extreme leads to diminished thriving; the goal is to find the middle way between these extremes. Review the scale below, and consider if any of the five keys are actually becoming challenges themselves.

Undercultivated keys need practice to increase their use; you may need to practice moderation for those that have become overcultivated.

UNDERCULTIVATED ———————————————— ♀ ———————————————— OVERCULTIVATED

Intention

| Wandering with no set direction | -3 | -2 | -1 | ♀ | 1 | 2 | 3 | Too much focus can lead to myopia |

Awareness

| Blind to the cues that can set your course | -3 | -2 | -1 | ♀ | 1 | 2 | 3 | Overwhelm of data points leads to analysis paralysis |

Boundaries

| Constant invitation for interruptions and distractions | -3 | -2 | -1 | ♀ | 1 | 2 | 3 | Rigidity misses opportunities for new inputs and collaboration |

Courage

| Fear of the unknown keeps us stagnant | -3 | -2 | -1 | ♀ | 1 | 2 | 3 | Ignoring reasonable fears opens us to risk |

Discipline

| All play and no work leaves us drifting through life | -3 | -2 | -1 | ♀ | 1 | 2 | 3 | All work and no play saps our joy |

NOW FOR YOUR PROJECT:
APPLYING THE FIVE KEYS TO THE FIVE CHALLENGES

The five keys and five challenges will be a theme you'll see running throughout this field guide. Unfortunately, the challenges will show up in some form in each and every project you take on. But the good news is you now know the keys to use to unlock those challenges.

Remember the mnemonic:
I-A-B-C-D

In order to finish any project you'll need:

Intention
to decide what work is important to you.

Awareness
to know where you shine and what tends to trip you up.

Boundaries
to create the space you need to get your best work done.

Courage
to show up despite your fears, and do your best work.

Discipline
to take consistent and purposeful action.

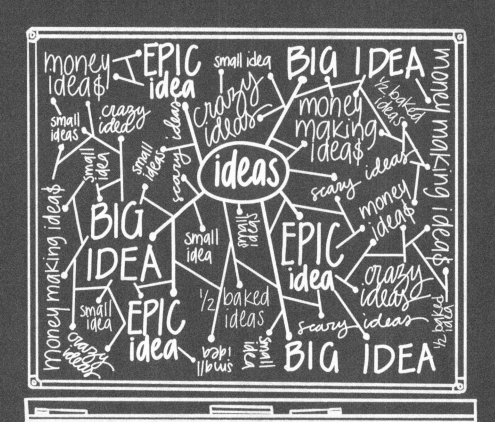

We're paradoxical creatures. On the one hand, we all want to do our best work.
On the other hand, we often avoid doing it.

PICK AN IDEA THAT MATTERS TO YOU

It's not that we don't know what matters
or have enough ideas — we likely have
more than we know what to do with.
The real challenge is choosing one idea
from everything we want to do, and
moving that one to done.

WHAT'S KEEPING YOU FROM YOUR BEST WORK?

What is creating the gap between your big picture and your day-to-day reality?

To pick an idea that matters, the part of you that wants to thrive and do your best work will have to overcome the part of you that wants to play it safe, be comfortable, and not ruffle any feathers.

Thrashing = the emotional flailing and meta work we do

The more an idea matters to you, the more you'll thrash. What's really going on is that we're working out our own head trash — the fears, impostor syndrome, and (sometimes) unconscious perceptions of our own inadequacies.

Creative Constipation = the pain of not doing your best work

We take in ideas and inspiration that get converted into aspirations, goals, and projects, and at a certain point they start to back up on us. We get toxic. We don't want to take in any more ideas. We don't want to do any more projects. We don't want to set any more goals or plans.

Failure ≠ a mark of character
Failure = a sign that something was out of alignment

Failure is inevitable, and if you're not failing and making the occasional bad decision, you're not doing your best work. The gift of failure is that it reveals what matters to you, shows you when you're out of alignment, and reveals a growth edge.

Thrashing is a sign that you're doing something that matters to you and that you'll need to show up powerfully to get it done.

HONE YOUR AWARENESS

At what point of a project are you most likely to thrash?

☐ Before the start of a project?
☐ In the midst of a project?
☐ At the end of a project?
☐ All of the above?

What are the warning signs that you're about to go into a thrash crash?
How might you stave these off?

_____

_____

_____

_____

Think about a time when you felt creatively constipated.
What had you stuck? How did it feel? What helped you through it?

_____

_____

_____

_____

What gifts have you received from a recent or important failure?
What did you learn? Be descriptive.

_____

_____

_____

_____

DISPLACEMENT IS YOUR FRIEND (AFTER IT'S YOUR ENEMY)

Not choosing costs you far more in the long run than choosing and finishing one significant project at a time. We can't run away from displacement, but we can use it to start finishing our best work.

Displacement
Every action I choose
displaces others
I could do in this same
space and time

can lead to

Discernment
I get to choose what
significant projects I work
on and how I
spend my time on them

When the struggle of displacement comes (and it will), remember these three things:
1. Everything you do displaces something else you could have done.
2. The work that really matters will take a concerted amount of time to finish.
3. The more you channel your energy towards one project, the faster you'll finish it and therefore can move on to the next project.

Displacement — the fact that doing something now excludes doing anything else — can help you focus on what matters, but only after you accept the limitations of time and energy.

◈ HOW MANY BEST-WORK PROJECTS DO YOU HAVE?

Displacement is not just at play with how we spend our days but also our lives. Whole Earth Catalog creator, Stewart Brand, suggested that significant, impactful ideas will require at least five years of focused action to complete.[1]

Determine how many best-work projects you have in you:

$$(85 - \underline{\hspace{2cm}}) \div 5 = \underline{\hspace{4cm}}$$

Your current age   Number of significant projects
you have left (round down)

---

[1] *Wired* magazine founder Kevin Kelly attributed this to Stewart Brand in Tim Ferriss's *Tools of Titans: The Tactics, Routines, and Habits of Billionaires, Icons, and World-Class Performers* (New York: Houghton Mifflin Harcourt, 2016).

TO TRADE UP, YOU HAVE TO LET GO

To get some headway with your best work, you have to fight the natural inclination to work on *all the things*. To make real progress on any idea you'll need to let others go. The exercises on the following pages walk you through that process step by step.

Step 1: List all the things
Capture all your ideas and potential projects in one spot.

Step 2: Reduce your list
Cull your list to the top 3–5 best-work options.

Step 3: Pick your focus project
Select one project to focus on for the next 12 weeks (as you go through this book).

⏲ Give yourself two uninterrupted hours for this exercise.

⬤ STEP 1: LIST ALL THE THINGS

Think beyond "professional" ideas and projects — yard and house projects, community initiatives, events with your community, traveling to Nepal, sorting your finances, or getting a puppy all count. It can be items on your bucket list, but they don't have to be bucket-list level.

On a blank piece of paper capture every idea and possible project.

- Big and small
- Personal and professional
- The shoulds and the coulds
- The projects that have been started, stalled, or stored away

After you have a first pass, take a break and look at the list again.
Is there anything else?

➕ To make sure you're considering all aspects of your life you may want to download the Wheel of Life exercise from the Resources page. It can help you see if any of the ten areas of your life might be out of alignment and needing attention.

⬡ STEP 2: REDUCE YOUR LIST

Once you have your list, ask yourself the following questions and cross out the items that meet the criteria of these questions:

---

1. Which of these items wouldn't actually hurt at all if you cut them?

2. Which of these items would you feel relieved to no longer be carrying?

3. Which of these items are "shoulds" or items that relate to other people's priorities (OPP), but you don't see how they'll directly lead to your thriving?

4. Which of these items are good ideas but don't relate to something that frustrates, annoys, angers, inspires, nourishes, or calls to you?

5. Which of these are things that some previous version of yourself put there that aren't relevant for where you are right now?

Feeling a little lighter? Reward yourself with a short break and come back one last time to review the list and questions again. Are there any others that should be crossed off?

Rewrite your list so it only includes ideas and projects that made the cut.
For the projects you've let go, there's no need to see them anymore.

You have to let go of projects and ideas that aren't allowing you to thrive so you can trade up to the projects that do.

◉ STEP 3: PICK YOUR PROJECT

Now you'll need to select just one project. You can always come back to the others on your (shorter) list. See chapter 5 for more information on sizing your project, but for now, look for a project (or project chunk) you can complete in 12 weeks. From your updated list, select 3–5 quarter-sized projects, label them A-B-C and so on, and use the chart below to get down to one.

	PROJECT				
Imagine that you're celebrating with a friend or loved one the most important thing you've done over the last year. If you could only pick one project on the list, which would it be?	A	B	C	D	E
Which of the items on the list causes the most gut-level anguish when you consider cutting it from the list completely?	A	B	C	D	E
Which of the items on the list are you most likely to wake up for two hours earlier, stay up for two hours later, or steal time elsewhere to create two hours to do?	A	B	C	D	E
Which of the items on the list, if finished, will matter the most in five years, in terms of having done it or how it sets up your future self for thriving?	A	B	C	D	E
Which of the items on the list is worth claiming one of your remaining "significant project" slots? (See page 27.)	A	B	C	D	E

In the case of a tie, go with the idea that wins on the third question, because it's better to get momentum on one idea that you'll create time for than others you won't.

Once you've made your choice:

- Circle the idea you've chosen to work on
- Date the paper you have been using
- Take a picture of the paper so you have a digital copy and put the physical piece of paper somewhere you will see it a few times a week.

➕ You can find a download link to the Pick Your Project worksheet on the Resources page.

WHAT TO DO WITH THE OTHER PROJECTS ON YOUR LIST

"Not Now" Isn't the Same Thing as "No."
Picking one idea displaces others you might have chosen right now. But deciding not to work on an idea frees up energy and focus to intentionally finish and work on another in the future.

What to Do with Your Collection of Smaller or Almost Finished Projects?
You likely had a few projects on your list after Step 2 that were smaller than quarter-sized.

1. Use the quarter-sized project you selected to get comfortable with the processes and methodology in this field guide. Then after you finish you can apply the same to these smaller projects so you can check them off your list.

2. Sometimes having a small or unfinished project can be a distraction — not allowing us to make progress on anything else. Determine what would be needed to get some or all of these projects to done and do that before continuing on.

NAME YOUR PROJECT

What do you want to accomplish?
Keep this rough for now, we'll hone the goal as we go. Some examples:
I want to write a book. I want to start a business.
I want to get a promotion. I want to clean out the basement.

_____

_____

_____

_____

_____

Why does this project matter to you?

_____

_____

_____

_____

_____

_____

Who will benefit from this project, and how?

_____

_____

_____

_____

_____

_____

PART 2 →

PLANNING YOUR PROJECT

Where
is this project
taking me?

What
does success
look like?

When
am I committing
to get it done?

Who
is going to help me
see it through?

Before you can determine the HOW of going from idea to done you'll first need to address the WHERE, WHAT, WHEN, and WHO.

CONVERT YOUR IDEA INTO A PROJECT

You've chosen your best-work idea;
now it's time to convert it into a project
that you can finish.

◉ WHERE IS THIS PROJECT TAKING ME?

Your project needs a goal that will help you identify where you are headed. But not all goals are created equal; some formulations of goals get us to done better than others. A SMART goal provides the details you'll need to prioritize, implement, and track progress against.

A SMART goal is simple, meaningful, actionable, realistic, and trackable.[1]

Review the idea you wrote down at the end of the last chapter.
Does it fit these criteria?

		Y	N
Simple You know exactly what you need to do to move forward with the idea.	*Do I know at a glance what my goal means?*	☐	☐
Meaningful You can look at it and quickly understand the importance of completing it.	*Does my goal connect with both my mind and my heart?*	☐	☐
Actionable It's immediately clear what action needs to be taken to accomplish the goal	*Does my goal begin with an action verb?*	☐	☐
Realistic The endpoint is achievable with the resources you have available.	*Do I have the time and resources I need to succeed?*	☐	☐
Trackable It's clear what progress means.	*What measurement am I tracking progress against?*	☐	☐

---

[1] George T. Doran first formulated the SMART goal framework in "There's a S.M.A.R.T. Way to Write Management's Goals and Objectives," Management Review 70, no. 11 (November 1981); 35–36. This version varies slightly from the original framework. See *Start Finishing* for more information.

TURN YOUR IDEA INTO A PROJECT WITH A SMART GOAL

Rewrite your idea from the last chapter as a goal using the SMART criteria.

My idea   My SMART Goal

_____   _____

_____   _____

_____   _____

_____   _____

If you get stuck you might try this popular formulation:

Finish   *(action verb)*   *(idea)*   by   *(date or other measurement)*
          _____   _____   _____

Example:

                                 book on the history
Finish   *writing*   *of cappuccino*   by   *the end of 2022*
          _____   _____   _____

Use your creativity and mental horsepower to figure out how to do the work, not to figure out what the work is.

WHAT DOES SUCCESS LOOK LIKE?

Now that you know where you are going, what do you want to have accomplished when you get there? How do you want to feel? How much time, energy, and attention do you realistically have to give?

Levels of Success   **Considerations**

Small Success

You accomplish the bare minimum   A string of small successes done with
of your goal.   coherence and intention can lead
                                       to much greater success down the line.

Moderate Success

You go a good way beyond the   The highest level of success you
bare minimum.   can achieve with just your own effort,
                                       resources, and advantages.

Epic Success

You knock it out of the park.   Epic success requires a team to help
A "tell your mama" moment.   you get there.

The higher the level of success, the more you'll need to do to achieve it.

CHOOSE YOUR LEVEL OF SUCCESS

Before you determine what level of success to aim for, you'll first need to identify what is required to reach each level. You might want to go back and check things against the realistic and actionable parts of your SMART goal.

Check your chosen level of success only after you know what each would look like *and* require of you.

Level of success	What does this level of success look like?	What does this level of success require?
☐ **Small**		
☐ **Medium**		
☐ **Epic**		

WHAT MIGHT GET IN YOUR WAY OF SUCCESS?

We all have things that can trip us up along the way. Better to plan for them now and think of strategies to address them rather than get caught up in the midst of a project.

List any known drag points*

List your success strategies

*We'll go deeper into drag points in a later chapter. For now, consider which of the five challenges might get in your way and how you might use one of the five keys to set yourself up for success.

WHEN ARE YOU COMMITTING TO GETTING IT DONE?

If a project doesn't have a start and a completion date, it's not likely that it's going to get done. Putting a date on an item makes it a commitment, which is one reason why some of us struggle with putting dates on items. If we can't follow through on the date, then we'll let ourselves and others down.

Commit to starting and finishing:

My Start Date _____   My End Date _____

Now that you have your start and end date:

Can you achieve your goal at your chosen
level of success in this time frame?   ☐ Yes   ☐ No

If no, what needs adjustment? (may be both)   ☐ Level of Success   ☐ Time Frame

Go back and rework your previous answers as needed.
(See why we suggested using a pencil?)

Does Your Project Need More Than 12 Weeks?
For the purposes of the exercises in this guide we've suggested selecting a project that fits within a 12-week time frame. But many best work projects require a much longer span of time. As we'll cover when we get to the project pyramid, larger-scale projects will need to be broken down into more manageable subprojects (chunks). What chunk of your best-work project could you feasibly get done in a 12-week span of time? Go back and readjust your goal or level of success as needed.

WHO IS GOING TO HELP YOU SEE IT THROUGH?

We can only reach a certain limit of success alone. To reach real and sustained success you'll need the assistance of others — you need a success pack.

Your success pack needs four types of people:

👁 Guides: vision that comes from experience

People you look up to that have walked the road a little longer than you have. While helpful to be able to communicate directly with everyone on your success pack, you might consider a guide (living or dead) just because they inspire you.

⚙ Peers: sounding boards and brainstorm partners

People at your approximate level of accomplishment or skill who can and will regularly contribute to your project. Peers make great accountability buddies (if the relationship supports regular communication). Consider peers from outside your discipline to offer fresh perspectives.

👍 Supporters: a helping pair of hands

People who are doing work with and for you to help you get your work done. Consider people who can support you in other parts of your life so you can have time and space to do your work.

♥ Beneficiaries: inspiration to stay on course and finish

The specific people who will benefit from the completion of your work. Like guides, beneficiaries might inspire from afar. But if you have a specific person in mind you'll likely work harder to finish your work for them.

And yes, you can have one person overlap multiple groups. But try to make sure everyone has a primary job on the team.

◉ CHOOSE YOUR SUCCESS PACK

All projects benefit when you have a success pack behind you. And if you've chosen an epic level of success they will be essential. Wondering who to include in your success pack? Scan your network.

Map out everyone in your network — known and unknown. Start with those closest to you and then expand outward. Only write down people whose presence (real or imagined) would aid in your success. No naysayers here (more on these characters later).

You

People you know well (friends, family, teammates)

Acquaintances, colleagues, fellow group members

People you want to know (leaders in your field, historical figures)

MY SUCCESS PACK

Using the descriptions from page 44 select the people from your network scan who you want on your success pack for this project. You'll want to include three to five people from each group (guides, peers, supporters, beneficiaries).

Group	Candidates	How They Can Help
Guides	1. _____	_____
	2. _____	_____
	3. _____	_____
	4. _____	_____
	5. _____	_____
Peers	1. _____	_____
	2. _____	_____
	3. _____	_____
	4. _____	_____
	5. _____	_____
Supporters	1. _____	_____
	2. _____	_____
	3. _____	_____
	4. _____	_____
	5. _____	_____
Beneficiaries	1. _____	_____
	2. _____	_____
	3. _____	_____
	4. _____	_____
	5. _____	_____

⬤ ENROLL YOUR SUCCESS PACK

Now that you have identified who you would like to be in your success pack your next step is to let each person know what you are up to and ask for their help.

---

1. Let each person know they're a part of your success pack.

    - Let them know you're working on something and you would love their help.
    - Align on how they can help and about how often you'll need that help
    - Confirm they are willing and able to help.
    - If you have chosen a guide (living or dead) who is not accessible to you, determine how you'll bring their inspiration into your project.

---

2. Proactively communicate with your success pack.

    - It's not the job of your success pack to follow up with you and ask how you're doing; it's your job to keep them informed and engaged (unless they've agreed to be an accountability partner).
    - Some success pack members will require more or less communication. Set the terms at the start and stick to them.

➕ You can find a download link to the Building Your Success Pack worksheet on the Resources page.

COMPLETE YOUR PROJECT SCOPER

At this point you have:

- ✔ Gotten clear on the challenges that cause the air sandwich
- ✔ Learned how to use the five keys to unlock your best work
- ✔ Picked an idea that matters to you
- ✔ Converted your idea into a SMART goal
- ✔ Chosen a level of success for your project
- ✔ Set your start and finish dates
- ✔ Built your success pack

Take all this information and complete your **Project Scoper,** your one-page reference document to guide you during the rest of the planning process.

➕ You can find a download link to the Project Scoper worksheet on the Resources page.

PROJECT SCOPER

Project: _____

Start Date: _____   End Date: _____   Level of Success: Small ☐   Moderate ☐   Epic ☐

Project Goals

_____
_____
_____
_____
_____
_____
_____

Priorities the Project Aligns With

_____
_____
_____
_____
_____
_____
_____

Known Dragpoints

_____
_____
_____
_____
_____
_____
_____

Success Strategies

_____
_____
_____
_____
_____
_____
_____

Success Pack Candidates

Guides
_____
_____
_____

Peers
_____
_____
_____

Supporters
_____
_____
_____

Beneficiaries
_____
_____
_____

How They Can Help

Guides
_____
_____
_____

Peers
_____
_____
_____

Supporters
_____
_____
_____

Beneficiaries
_____
_____
_____

The 3 essential skills to bending time

CHUNKING → LINKING → SEQUENCING

Splitting projects into coherent, doable parts.

Joining chunks together so that they hang together.

Linking chunks together into a logical order in space & time

MAKE SPACE
FOR YOUR PROJECT

Before you can start doing your best
work or create a roadmap to get you there,
you'll need to create the space for it.
Chunking, linking, and sequencing are the
key skills that will help you create space
and build plans that work.

THE PROJECT PYRAMID

The project pyramid builds on chunking, linking, and sequencing because it shows how bigger projects contain smaller projects, as well as how smaller chunks tie together to build momentum.

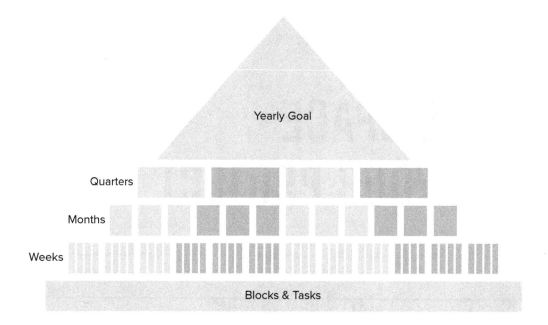

Best-Work Projects Work Best at the Quarterly Level

A **best-work** project may stretch across a year or even multiple years, but a single **quarter** is the ideal time horizon for making *progress* on a best-work project. You'll still need to break that goal into smaller chunks that are doable within more discrete time frames — ones you can get your arms (and brain) around.

Use **months** for more distinct goals or subprojects of your quarter-sized projects.

Divide your **weeks** into actionable tasks and blocks that generate momentum to move your larger projects across the finish line.

⬤ SMALLER CHUNKS OF TIME CAN BE SLIPPERY

We can't mark seconds, minutes, hours, and days very well, yet those are the chunks of time that most time-management systems and many of our practices try to get us to use. When chunking down beyond the weekly level it is better to convert from those time conventions to blocks and tasks.

Block = a chunk of work that can be done in two hours

Task = a chunk of work that can be done in fifteen minutes

Identify the Chunks in Your To-Do List

To build momentum on any project, you'll want to chunk down the items on your to-do list to blocks and tasks.

1. Print out your current to-do list or grab your printed list/planner, and a pencil.

2. Next to each entry, mark what size chunk from the project pyramid you've captured.

3. Identify the items that need to be chunked down to the block or task size and estimate the number of blocks that might be required.

We don't work on projects; we work on chunks of projects linked together in the right sequence.

◉ HOW COMMON PROJECT WORDS TIE TOGETHER

The simplest expression of a chunk is a verb-noun construct because it tells you the action that's being taken on something. Verbs often give an indication to how big a chunk of work is, and certain verbs follow and contain others.

Verb It

1. Go back to your to-do list. Do you know what action needs to be taken to be able to cross it off your list?

2. Re-write your list so each item starts with a verb. Use the list of Common Project Verbs if you get stuck.

I want nouns without verbs on your action lists to be something that you'll forever be unable to tolerate without fixing.

Common Project Verbs

Quarter- or month-sized project verbs

for work needing a few week- or month-sized projects to complete:

Rework	Launch / Ship	Kick off
Develop	Build	Move / Relocate
Strategize	Publish (books, articles)	

Week-sized project verbs

for work needing at least one, but no more than five, blocks per project segment:

Research	Plan	Promote
Decide on	Design	Edit
Collaborate with	Analyze / Evaluate	Apply
Create	Coordinate	

Task verbs

for work that can be done in fifteen minutes:

Email / Mail	Check / Review	Print
Call / Text	Find	Buy
Sort	Compile	Ask / Thank
Read	Schedule	Upload / Download
Send / Share	Make	

THE FIVE PROJECTS RULE

The Five Projects Rule is shorthand for "no more than five active projects per timescale" and helps prioritize and plan projects.

No More than Five

The upper limit - not the default

3 Professional
2 Personal

Active Projects

Those you are actively pushing forward.

Remember to Verb it!

Per Timescale

Year
Quarter
Month
Week

◉ APPLYING THE FIVE PROJECTS RULE

Most people won't complete more than five total projects per timescale. Since how many projects we *finish* is more important than how many we start, we do ourselves no favors by committing to more projects than we'll be able to do.

Use the space below to list the active projects you have at each time scale.

Remember:

- Five is the limit, not the requirement.
- Start each project with a verb to make it active.
- Displacement is your friend (after it's your enemy).

	This Year	This Quarter	This Month	This Week
1.				
2.				
3.				
4.				
5.				

Use this exercise to wrestle with the fact that you may be carrying more than you can handle. You'll revisit this exercise again after working through your best-work roadmap in the next chapter.

➕ If you want to see how your projects stack up on the project pyramid, download the Project Pyramid Quarterly worksheet from the Resources page.

CONVERT YOUR WEEKLY SCHEDULE INTO COHERENT BLOCKS

It's the weekly level where you'll actually be able to do the work necessary to move the needle on your best-work project. Use these four types of blocks to gain momentum at the weekly level.

Focus *90–120 min*

The smallest unit of meaningful, coherent work.

These fuel your best work. No or too few focus blocks = no finished best work.

You'll need energy to do high-level work that requires focus.

Social *90–120 min*

A block of time used for interacting with others in real time.

Spending time with your friends, family, colleagues, and tribe is valuable.

When we are primed energetically to be with others.

Admin *30–60 min*

Short blocks of time used to complete tasks that need to get done.

Work that supports your best work but isn't your best work itself.

Lower energy work that doesn't require heavy lifting.

Recovery *variable*

Activities that recharge our batteries and allow us to do our best work.

Be intentional about replenishing energy expended by the other blocks.

Think energy input vs. output.

CREATE A WEEKLY SCHEDULE THAT WORKS FOR YOU

Before you can figure out when you'll do your best work, you'll need to carve some space into your schedule — identify where all your blocks are and/or should be. For this exercise you'll need to start with a blank weekly schedule. To make things easier, download our **Weekly Block Scheduler** (see Resources).

☐ **1. Plot your time-bound commitments**

Fill in any regular or recurring appointments, meetings, or activities. Include things like morning and evening routines, commuting, kids' sports schedules, etc.

☐ **2. Identify your existing blocks**

Determine what types of blocks these events correspond to. You might consider using some sort of visual cue such as color coding or icons to easily denote the difference.

☐ **3. Claim your best-work focus blocks**

Look for at least three two-hour blocks you can claim for your best work. These will need to be times where you'll be uninterrupted and have the energy to do high-level work.

☐ **4. Fill in the gaps**

Use the best practices on the next page to fill in the rest of your blocks (admin, social, and recovery).

☐ **5. Make adjustments as you go**

This will be an iterative process with the goal of eventually finding an optimal schedule for *you* based on the realities of *your life*. Depending on the amount and strength of your constraints, you may have to lock in and change one block at a time.

➕ You can find a download link to the Weekly Block Scheduler worksheet on the Resources page.

BEST PRACTICES FOR CREATING YOUR WEEKLY BLOCK SCHEDULE

→ **Leave contingency time** in your week to manage challenges and unexpected events.

→ **Three focus blocks per week** give your project momentum.

→ Some kinds of projects seem like Admin, but they actually require **focus blocks** (think organizing the "closet of doom" which requires a lot of planning, conversation, trying things out, etc.).

→ **Social blocks** make for great bookends to other blocks because most of us honor commitments to other people more than we honor commitments to ourselves.

→ Put your **social blocks** where you're most fit for human consumption.

→ Sandwiching an **admin block** between two social blocks can create a coherent flow for both because there's often some type of admin work that follows social blocks.

→ Avoid putting an **admin block** first thing in the morning, but if you must, be intentional about processing it, looking only for items that are relevant for the day.

→ As a general rule, plan on a **recovery block** for every two focus or social blocks.

Focus blocks are the fuel for your best work
and the anchors in your schedule.

HOLDING SPACE

Making space for your project will likely displace other projects you could be doing. Your best-work project is one of the (maximum) five projects you have committed to this next quarter.

What other projects have you committed to working on during this same time period? Remember the Five Projects Rule.

_____

_____

_____

Are there other projects not included above that need to be moved to a future quarter? Tip: Schedule a date in the future to re-engage with these projects so they don't compete for the valuable space you've worked hard to make.

_____

_____

_____

What are the main action verbs associated with your project? Remember: verbs help identify the length of time a chunk of work might take. (More on plotting these in your project roadmap in the next chapter.)

_____

_____

_____

Where have you identified focus blocks in your schedule? What steps will you take to hold that space open to work on your project? Remember: focus blocks fuel your best work.

_____

_____

_____

YOUR GATES

How to leverage your unique abilities and talents to achieve your goals.

YOUR BUDGET

How to finance your goals.

YOUR CAPACITY

How to create a plan that works for you.

Three important elements inform how you will get where you are going. Think of them as navigation markers for your personal roadmap.

BUILD YOUR PROJECT ROADMAP

It's time to convert your vertical list of to-dos into a horizontal, time-based plan — one that chunks, links, and sequences the project over time so you won't have to do the sequencing work every time you look at it.

 **BUILD FROM YOUR GATES**

Rather than start your project in hard mode, why not take the upper hand by playing to your strengths? Strengths come in different varieties. Use the acronym GATES to help you consider what you should base your projects on.

Genius

What seems to be an expression of an inner creative force.

Affinities

What you're drawn to do.

Talents

What seem to be your native skills or capabilities.

Expertise

What you've learned through experience and practice.

Strengths

What seems to come easy for you.

Name All Your Gates

Take a blank piece of paper and write down everything that comes to mind when you think of your genius, affinities, talents, expertise, and strengths. Don't limit yourself to just professional skills. Aim for at least 15.

Save this list, reference it in future planning, and add to it as you develop new GATES.

How will you use your GATES to make your project flow more easily?

 **GATES to Goals**

How will you use your GATES to make your project flow more easily?

1. **List Your Goals for This Project**
Start with the end in mind. What do you hope to achieve through this project? Use the table below or download our **Leverage Your GATES** worksheet from the Resources page.

2. **Pick Your GATES**
Which of your GATES will best set you up for success with this project?

3. **Determine the Method**
Based on your GATES, what are the best methods (actions, strategies, tactics, techniques) for you to go about achieving your goal?

GATES	Method	Goals

➕ You can find a download link to the Leverage Your GATES worksheet on the Resources page.

BUILD A BUDGET FOR YOUR PROJECT

Creating a budget for your project helps avoid snags and stall-outs. It's an awareness-generating process, especially when you walk through the checklist of costs that just about any project may have. Consider the following categories:

Category	Considerations
Professional support Administrative assistants, editors, copywriters, photographers, lawyers, etc.	Hiring professionals can make a big difference in the quality of the end product or the ease in completing it.
Tools and apps Physical tools or digital programs needed to get the work done or make it easier	Paying for these items versus borrowing or creating workarounds can often save your time, energy, and attention.
Personal support and caretakers House cleaning, yard care, grocery delivery, childcare, elder care, pet sitters, etc.	These services allow you to spend more focused time on your best work knowing your loved ones are safe and cared for.
Lodging, offices, and table rent Temporary office, co-working space, hotel stay, or coffee/tea (table rent) at your local coffee house	Get your work done in a place away from the interruptions and distractions of daily life.
Food Meal delivery, hired meal prep, take-out, morning coffee	Saves time and energy spent in preparing and cleaning up meals.

◈ Create Your Project Budget

☐ 1. Determine your total budget.

How much money do you have available that you would be willing to spend to finish this project?

☐ 2. Identify possible expenses.

a. Review the categories from the previous page and list the specific support or tools you might need to complete this project.

b. Identify how each would benefit you and your project. Would it save you time? Would it enhance quality? Would it free you of interruptions or distractions?

☐ 3. Estimate your expenses.

Include a cost for each item listed above (estimate as best you can).

☐ 4. Total your estimated expenses.

Add the estimated costs for all your anticipated expenses to get your total costs.

☐ 5. Do you have the funds to cover your expenses?

YES: Your total estimated expenses are equal or less than your total budget.

NO: Your total estimated expenses are more than your total budget.

When Your Costs Exceed Your Budget: Re-Evaluate

If you find yourself with a budget shortfall, consider these questions for how you might adjust:

1. Can you increase your budget to offset the difference?

2. Can you reduce or remove some of the estimated costs? How would this impact your time, energy, and attention?

3. Can you upgrade this project to a higher time scale to account for additional time you might need to do the work?

4. Do you need to have another project in front of this one to create funds to fuel this project?

➕ You can find a download link to the *Project Budget* worksheet on the *Resources* page.

◉ BUILD AROUND PLANNING NEEDS

Use deadlines to guide your project, but remember that it's your capacity that drives your project no matter what the deadline is.

Planning based on deadline

Plan backwards from some point in the future (deadline) to identify the milestones and targets you'll need to hit to make your deadline.

Planning based on capacity

Plan forward based on the number of focus blocks (capacity) you will have to make progress on your goals.

Deadline or Capacity?

Use backwards planning (based on deadline) only if you check yes to one or more of the following questions.

	YES	NO
Do you need to constrain the size of your project because you have limited focus blocks available to work on it?	☐	☐
Are you having a hard time identifying the milestones and deadlines you'll need to hit?	☐	☐
Is your project anchored to a specific end date such as taxes, holidays, recurring deadlines?	☐	☐

Don't Forget to Account for Relay Time

When you're working with collaborators — and almost all best-work projects have collaborators — make sure to build relay time into your roadmap.

Relay time = the waiting time that happens every time a project changes hands

Reduce relay time with a good handoff:
- Be clear and specific about what you need and when you need a response.
- Include next steps and if necessary who is involved at later stages of the project.
- Use channels that are best suited for these types of communications and where others are likely to see your requisition.

When we build from our capacity rather than the deadline, we get closer to carrying the amount of projects we can actually finish.

HOW TO BUILD YOUR PROJECT ROADMAP

With your GATES, budget, and capacity in mind, use the seven steps on the following pages to to break your project down into the chunks you'll get done during the blocks you carved into your schedule.

Step 1: Start Your Chunk List

Define the chunks that make up your project. Using action verbs, list all the items that need to be done to complete your project. Don't worry about when they'll be done or what order they need to be done in, because that will slow you down.

Step 2: Sort and Link Your Chunks

Join chunks together so that they hang together. Rewrite your list so related chunks are grouped together. Note how month-sized chunks contain week-sized chunks and link with other month-sized clumps (see step 4).

Step 3: Sequence Your Chunks

Arrange chunks in the order that they need to be done. Take your joined chunks and determine in what order they make most sense to do in. Look at how the verbs relate to one another.

Step 4: Clump Your Chunks

The process of organizing smaller chunks by the larger chunks that contain them. If chunking was breaking the building blocks apart, clumping is now putting those pieces together into larger linked units, which helps you see the higher-level time perspective.

 **Step 5:** Upgrade Your Clumps

Do your clumps (or your project) need to move up a time perspective? Check your clumps against these potential upgrade triggers to determine if an upgrade is needed.

	Trigger for Upgrade	What upgrade is needed?
You have no idea how long it will take to do the clump.	☐	
You're not competent at the work involved to complete the clump.	☐	
The clump depends on someone else completing a significant chunk of the work.	☐	
The clump contains more than five chunks.	☐	
One of the chunks in the clump will take a majority of that time horizon to complete.	☐	

The point of a plan isn't to straitjacket you but to give you the levers to drive your project to done.

Step 6: Overlay Your Chunks on a Timeline

Check that the sequence of chunks still appears coherent and logical.

Does the sequence still work when put in the context of a timeline?

Project Goal

Month 1	Month 2	Month 3
Month-sized Chunks or Clumps	Month-sized Chunks or Clumps	Month-sized Chunks or Clumps

1 2 3 4   1 2 3 4   1 2 3 4

Step 7: Schedule Your Chunks

Commit to your project by putting your chunks on your schedule. Try not to schedule too far in advance as you'll likely get frustrated when reality doesn't look like your plans. (More on this in chapter 8.)

➕ You can find a download link to the 12-Week Project Roadmap worksheet on the Resources page.

12-WEEK PROJECT ROAD MAP

Project: _____

Month 1

_____
_____
_____
_____
_____
_____
_____
_____

Month 2

_____
_____
_____
_____
_____
_____
_____
_____

Month 3

_____
_____
_____
_____
_____
_____
_____
_____

Week 1: _____
_____

Week 2: _____
_____

Week 3: _____
_____

Week 4: _____
_____

Week 5: _____
_____

Week 6: _____
_____

Week 7: _____
_____

Week 8: _____
_____

Week 9: _____
_____

Week 10: _____
_____

Week 11: _____
_____

Week 12: _____
_____

Reality check: Drag points are the natural places where reality will push against your plans.

KEEP FLYING BY ACCOUNTING FOR DRAG POINTS

It's time to put your plan to the test in the real world. This is when the beauty of your pristine project plan butts up against reality, and all the other tensions and people and beliefs that inhabit your world.

YOUR NO-WIN SCENARIOS ARE KEEPING YOU FROM THRIVING

Many of us ingrain in ourselves a story that to be successful in our work or lives, we have to give up something important to us. These limiting beliefs hold us back not just from success but from happiness.

No-Win Scenarios	Impact
The Success Will Wreck My Relationships tale If I succeed I will hurt someone I care about. **The Success Will Wreck My Health tale*** If I succeed I'll deplete my mental, emotional, spiritual, and physical resources.	We default to the worst-case scenario before we know if it's even a realistic outcome.
The Starving Artist myth If my art starts selling well, it means I've sold out. **The Nice Guys/Gals Finish Last myth** In order to succeed I have to compromise who I am.	We play small in order to preserve our virtues.
The Rich People Are Bad People myth Financial success means taking advantage of others. **The What If I Can't Do It Again trap** If I succeed this time I'll need to succeed every time.	We avoid mastery in pursuit of mediocrity.

*This no-win scenario revealed itself after the publication of *Start Finishing*; we're excited to include it here for the first time!

Reframe Your No-Win Scenarios

Name the stories you're telling yourself about your project and what actions you might take to address them.

What no-win scenario have I created?	What actions can I take to address this?

DON'T BE "DOWN WITH OPP" (OTHER PEOPLE'S PRIORITIES)

Similar to our own Competing Priorities (chapter 2), OPP (other people's priorities) can conflict with our own best work. But there are often ways to weave OPP into our work and convert conflict into cooperation.

Identify the OPP in Your World

We all have them. It's not a matter of *if* but how many and how we address them. List all the possible OPP that will conflict with your project. Then for each, answer the following questions:

- What is the priority?
- Who owns this priority?
- Do you accept it as a valid but competing priority with your project?
    - If yes, how will you incorporate it into your schedule?
    - If no, what boundary can you establish to minimize the OPP's effect on your project?
- Can you find a way to weave this OPP (the person and their priority) into your project?

Every ounce of energy you use grappling with a naysayer is much better spent working on your project and interacting with your success pack.

 **DERAILERS AND NAYSAYERS**

If your success pack is the rocket fuel that propels your project, your derailers
and naysayers are the winds actively working against you.

Derailers

Well-meaning people whose "help"
and "feedback" throw you off course.

Naysayers

People who are *actively against* your
project (and let you know it).

Who Are Your Derailers and Naysayers?

List all the people you can think of who might fall into the derailer or naysayer camp
and create strategies you might use to mitigate or reverse their impact.

Who	Derailer (D) or Naysayer (N)	Strategies to Employ with This Person

SET YOURSELF UP FOR SUCCESS WITH A PROJECT PREMORTEM

Now that you've identified the drag points that might plague your project, it's a good time to revisit your project plan with those things in mind.

Use the space below or download your **Project Premortem** worksheet (see Resources).

Have you created any no-win scenarios for yourself? How might you detangle them?

_____

_____

_____

_____

Have you picked a method of doing your project that's especially hard for you?
How might you start from and leverage your GATES?

_____

_____

_____

_____

What OPP do you need to account for? How might you align OPP with your project?

_____

_____

_____

_____

Are there any derailers and (real) naysayers you need to account for?
List them by name and how you'll address them.

_____

_____

_____

_____

Are you carrying any projects that you can let go of to keep them from bogging you down?

_____

_____

_____

_____

Are there any bad or unhelpful stories you're telling yourself — I'm a flake, I'm no good at planning, Who do I think I am to do this? — and what will you do to counteract these stories?

_____

_____

_____

_____

Are there any budgetary constraints that might impact your time, energy, and attention? Have you adjusted your plan accordingly?

_____

_____

_____

_____

Do you have the number of focus blocks needed to complete the project in the time allotted and at the Level of Success you committed to? If not, what needs adjusting?

_____

_____

_____

_____

➕ You can find a download link to the Project Premortem worksheet on the Resources page.

PART 3 ➤

WORKING THE PLAN

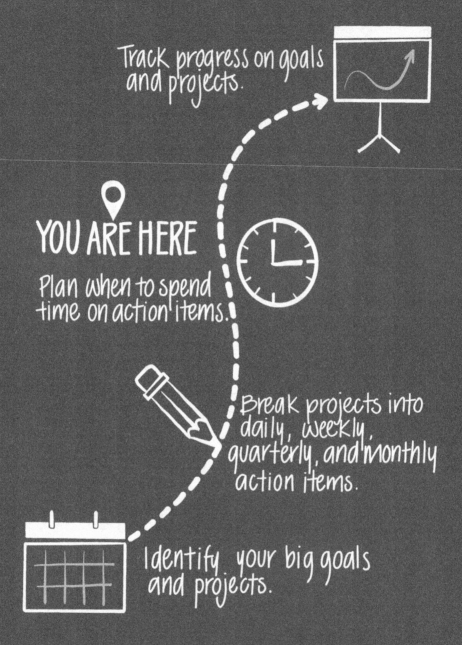

Track progress on goals and projects.

YOU ARE HERE

Plan when to spend time on action items.

Break projects into daily, weekly, quarterly, and monthly action items.

Identify your big goals and projects.

To start doing your best work, you have to start weaving your project into your total work-life schedule.

WEAVE YOUR PROJECT INTO YOUR SCHEDULE

You've spent the preceding sections figuring out what your project is, why you're doing it, what it consists of, and what might derail you. Now it's time to integrate your planned project components and actionable steps into your calendar.

BATCHING AND STACKING WORK INCREASE YOUR EFFICIENCY

The first step for integrating your project tasks into your schedule is to consider which tasks you can batch or stack. Certain similar tasks are best done in batches. Others you can stack together using different kinds of physical and mental resources simultaneously.

Batching

The process of doing *similar kinds* of work in a contiguous stretch of time. Batching minimizes the context shifting that happens when we go back and forth between unrelated tasks. *Think triaging and processing emails.*

Stacking

The process of doing *dissimilar kinds* of work in the same stretch of time. Stacking creates intention for the kinds of activities that can be done simultaneously versus inefficient multitasking. *Think taking a conference call while going for a walk.*

INTEGRATE BATCHING AND STACKING TO MAXIMIZE YOUR SCHEDULE

Which activities can you do in batches?

_____

_____

_____

_____

_____

_____

_____

_____

_____

Which activities can you stack together?

_____

_____

_____

_____

_____

_____

_____

_____

_____

A FROG A DAY...

Frogs are the tasks and chunks of projects that we really don't want to do — addressing them more frequently helps keep the dread-to-work ratio lower.

The longer the task sits on your list and the more time you invest in thinking about putting it off, the larger its (psychological) size — the frog gets bigger and harder to swallow.

If a task was going to take five minutes at first, then odds are it's going to take at least five minutes whenever you do it.

The "work" part of the equation stays the same. It's the "dread" that increases substantially with time.

Make a habit of catching your frogs early and often by regularly asking yourself these questions:

- What task, project, or reality am I avoiding?
- Why might I be avoiding this?
- When will I take care of this task?

If you know you have to swallow a frog, swallow it first thing in the morning. If there are two frogs, swallow the big one first. — Mark Twain

MAKE SURE YOUR ENVIRONMENT IS WORKING FOR YOU

Where you work has a big impact on your focus, momentum, and creativity. Are you actively creating the space to do your best work? When building the sort of environment that serves you best, consider these seven factors:

Sound

Do you prefer complete quiet or do you need ambient noise? What level or type of background noise fuels your work?

Smell

Are there different smells that help get you settled into your work? (Think smell of coffee, scented lotion, candles, essential oils, etc.)

Sunlight

Do you prefer ample light or does working in a darker room help you focus?

Clothing

What clothes provide comfort while also signalling the type of work you need to do?

Clutter/Organization

Do you work better in "organized chaos," a spartan environment, or somewhere in between?

Amount of Space

Are you more comfortable in smaller spaces or work nooks or does an expansive workspace help you think big?

Music

Does music help you get into flow? If so, what type of music? And does it depend on the type of work you need to do?

 **WHEN BEFORE WHAT**

Instead of planning based on *what* needs to be done, make your foundation *when* it's best for you to do certain kinds of work. Pay attention to your energy levels to understand the times of day and days of the week that are optimal for doing your best work.

What Time of Day Is Your Most Productive?

"The early bird gets the worm" may be a well-known idiom, but it's not entirely accurate for those who are not made for mornings. Which productive bird are you?

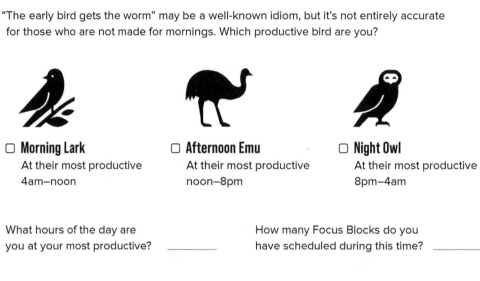

☐ **Morning Lark**
At their most productive
4am–noon

☐ **Afternoon Emu**
At their most productive
noon–8pm

☐ **Night Owl**
At their most productive
8pm–4am

What hours of the day are
you at your most productive? _____

How many Focus Blocks do you
have scheduled during this time? _____

➕ **Not sure which chronotype best matches your workflow? You might want to try heat mapping your day. Use our Productivity Heat Mapping tool on the Resources page.**

WHAT DAYS OF THE WEEK WORK BEST FOR YOU?

Some days of the week may be better to do certain kinds of work than other days.

On what days do you have the most creative, positive energy?	➜ Build the most focus blocks into these days
On which days are collaborators more available and "in the zone?"	➜ Batch follow-up and collaborative work on these days
What days do you consider "end-of-week" or ramp-down days?	➜ Schedule social maintenance vs. decision-making or strategy
What days provide the most opportunity to see the bigger picture?	➜ Schedule weekly and monthly planning when you can zoom up a time perspective
What days are you resting?	➜ Schedule at least one day per week; two or three might be what you need

First in *Priority* Doesn't Mean First in *Sequence*.

A few factors you might consider for determining the when for your most important tasks:

- Access to the right environment
- Times of day that best suit your natural chronotype
- Other projects or responsibilities already on your schedule
- Availability of collaborators or success pack members

↺ Now that you've uncovered the times and days that work best for you, go back to the Weekly Block Scheduler you created in chapter 5 and see how you might adjust your blocks or theme your days to better work on your schedule.

MOMENTUM PLANNING

Momentum Planning is the continual process of making and adjusting plans across all time perspectives. Each shift in timescale is a shift in perspective. When planning, the next highest timescale informs the *why* and the next lowest informs the *how*.

When you need clarity of purpose, shift up; when you need clarity of action steps, shift down.

Year	*Quarter*	*Month*
why	**why**	**why**
↑	↑	↑
Quarter	**Month**	**Week**
↓	↓	↓
how	**how**	**how**
Month	*Week*	*Blocks & Tasks*

You're committing to important projects you'll finish, not everything you might work on.

HOW TO DO YOUR FIRST ROUND OF MOMENTUM PLANNING

The hardest part of Momentum Planning is doing the first round, because it's not completely obvious where to start. Here's how to do your Momentum Planning if you're starting from scratch.

1. **Start with the month-level perspective.**
   It's big enough for context but small enough to not require planning a time to plan.

2. **Review and capture any deadlines or major events.**
   Look at the month ahead and account for any events that will pull you out of your normal routine for a day or more. These deadlines and events will influence how many blocks you'll have available and when they are.

3. **Review, adjust, and capture your five projects for the quarter.**
   This provides context for what your five projects for this month should be.

4. **Decide what your five projects for the month need to be.**
   Remember you don't have to fill up all five project slots — you are committing to doing projects, not just writing them down.

5. **Chunk your projects into week-sized chunks for every week of the month.**
   Not all month-sized projects will break down into 4 week-sized chunks. Use the Five Projects Rule to account for events and recurring projects which may fill in those slots.

6. **Review, reassess, and revise your weekly projects as needed.**
   You'll likely need to take a couple of passes, as the first pass is usually overoptimistic even when using the Five Projects Rule.

➕ If you are new to Momentum Planning and want to try it out, see the Resources page for links to our free Momentum Planners.

A CYCLE OF PLANNING AND REVIEWS BUILDS MOMENTUM

Reviews at each time perspective are built into the Momentum Planning Method. It's the regular reviews that fuel momentum because they allow you to reassess and adjust your plans and make mid-course corrections as necessary.

Don't fall into the trap of thinking that just because you didn't start the day, week, or month with a plan that you should tread water until the start of the next day, week, or month. Start where you are and build from there.

USE THE 5/10/15 SPLIT TO BUILD DAILY MOMENTUM

The *5/10/15 split* makes your Momentum Planning a breeze and helps you course correct when reality pushes against your plans.

The 5 Projects Rule

No more than five active projects per timescale.

10-minute check-in

A morning review to see if anything new popped up that requires adjustment to the plan previously set.

15-minute check-out

An end-of-day assessment of what was accomplished, what needs to be accounted for, and what needs to be reassessed.

If necessary, prioritize the check-out because we usually have a better perspective at the end of the day than at the beginning of the day.

➕ **You can find planning and review questions for all time perspectives including the Check-In and Check-Out on the Resources page.**

The steps we take today create a different path for tomorrow. Each step counts.

9

BUILD DAILY MOMENTUM

When we think about thriving, we tend to think big picture, but the reality is that it's the accumulation of purposeful and productive days that lead to our thriving. We become by doing, and the days are where the doing happens.

CELEBRATE SMALL WINS SO YOU CAN CELEBRATE BIGGER ONES

Intentionally celebrating the small wins along the way helps create the momentum to keep going through those rougher patches and enables us to celebrate big finishes.

Why It's Important to Celebrate the Small Wins

→ The small wins get you through the messy middle so that you can create the bigger wins.

→ If you can celebrate what may seem like insignificant wins, the more significant wins will be all the easier to acknowledge and celebrate.

Take a moment to acknowledge that you showed up, and in the midst of an over-distracted, over-pressured, and over-urgent world, you finished something that mattered.

THREE WAYS YOU CAN CELEBRATE YOUR SMALL WINS

It's easy to see what led to the big win when you've been celebrating and keeping up with all the small wins along the way.

1. **Create a win journal in which you highlight three wins every day.**
   Use your 15-minute check out to capture your wins each day or use our **Monthly Win Journal** (see the Resources page for a download link).

2. **Keep a project and/or streak tracker.**
   Track the daily habits you want to stick to that'll help you move your project forward.

3. **Share small wins with other people.**
   Keep your success pack updated on your successes throughout the project, not just at the end.

➕ You can find a link to the Monthly Win Journal (with built-in streak tracker) on the Resources page.

HABITS AND ROUTINES MAKE IT EASIER TO BUILD AND MAINTAIN MOMENTUM

Every choice we don't have to make lets us focus on things that actually matter. Habits and routines minimize decision fatigue and create longer periods of flow.

Habits = singular ingrained behaviors
Routines = a sequence of joined behaviors

Anchor Habits to Your Environment

As previously covered, your environment impacts your work. A scent or space can trigger a specific type of work. And certain tools are needed to do different types of work.

Environments = the containers we do habits in
Tools = the things that trigger certain habits

The major upshot of routines is that the only choice you need to make is to start the routine; the rest of the sequence has the inertia to complete itself.

CREATE YOUR ROUTINES

Create and maintain the defaults that work and minimize the ones that work against you.

1. List the activities you routinely do during different parts of your day.

   Use a blank piece of paper or our **Creating Your Routines** worksheet (see the Resources page for a download link) to track the routines you're already doing at different parts of your day:

   - Morning/Start of Day (examples: stretch, have coffee, journal, exercise, shower)
   - Work Warm-up (examples: review prior night check out, identify frog for the day)
   - Mid-Day (examples: lunch, take a walk, cach up with a friend)
   - Work Checkout (examples: final review of email, 15-minute checkout)
   - After Work (examples: commute home, make dinner, exercise, spend time with family)
   - End of Day (examples: read, wash face, meditate, stretch, clean up)

2. Identify what is serving or hampering your best work.

   Put a check next to the habits that fuel your productivity and an x mark next to those that don't.

3. Brainstorm ideal routines.

   Determine how you can amplify or reward what's working and moderate or replace those that are working against you.

4. Rewrite your lists.

   On a new sheet of paper, write down the routines that support your best work.

5. Remind yourself when and where it counts.

   Leave your lists in places where you can reference them during that time of day.

➕ You can find a link to the Creating Your Routines worksheet on the Resources page.

MINIMIZE INTERRUPTIONS AND DISTRACTIONS

To take control of your focus blocks you'll need to identify the entry points for diversions and develop strategies to minimize or eliminate them during times of deep work.

Interruptions = external diversions that keep us from doing our best work

These are things such as children walking into the room, incoming phone calls, and co-workers knocking on the door (despite the rule of no knocking if the door's closed).

Distractions = internal diversions that we allow ourselves

Email, social media, YouTube, past seasons of your favorite show, or the latest installment of your favorite book series fall into this category. None of these run into the room and tug on our shirt; we allow them to tug on us.

If we choose to be distracted, we're also choosing to not do our best work.

 **INTERRUPT INTERRUPTIONS**

As interruptions come from outside sources (like kids, pets, and bosses) you'll need to determine who or what might disrupt your work and then set and communicate boundaries needed during your focus time.

Who or what is most likely to interrupt you? (Be specific)

_____

_____

_____

_____

_____

_____

_____

_____

What boundaries do you need to establish and express?

_____

_____

_____

_____

_____

_____

_____

_____

➕ See chapter 9 of *Start Finishing* for tips on difficult conversations.

 **DEAL WITH DISTRACTIONS**

We rarely consciously choose to be distracted (by things like social media, TV, email), and we don't intend on being distracted for as long as we actually end up being distracted. The boundaries we need to create to disrupt them are with ourselves.

Eliminating distractions alone can generate the recommended three focus blocks per week needed to fuel a best-work project.

What are your most common distractions? (Be specific)

What tools or techniques can you employ to reduce or eliminate?

REMEMBER TO USE THE FIVE KEYS

The five keys are strategies you can employ each and every day to help you start finishing your best work.

Intention

Remind yourself why your time and this work is so important.

Awareness

Know what's working and what isn't and adjust accordingly.

Boundaries

Establish expectations, structures, and space to support your goals.

Courage

Show up each day and face the challenges that inevitably will appear.

Discipline

Stick with the plan, adjust when necessary. Repeat.

Before success, start finishing. After success, start finishing.

10

FINISH STRONG

Congratulations, you've crossed
the finish line! Rather than just jumping
to the next thing, it's time to
bask in the success you've created.

 **RUN A VICTORY LAP**

It's one of the most important, yet often overlooked, activities of a project. But not celebrating hurts us **and** the people who've been with us the whole race: *our success pack*. Those who've guided us and challenged us and supported us and received the benefits of our labors have been with us all along, and it's time for us to celebrate our success with them.

Where was your starting line?	Review your **Project Scoper** (chapter 5) and remind yourself of where you started.
What are you celebrating?	Read over your **Win Journal** (chapter 9) and see how all the little wins brought you to the finish line.
Who are you celebrating with?	Let your **Success Pack** (chapter 4) help you reflect on and amplify your successful finish.
How will you celebrate?	**Get Creative.** You get to decide how you want to recognize and be recognized for your accomplishment.

What we so often forget is that the victory lap isn't just about the victor but also the community.

Make Space to Transition Between Projects

Trying to start your next project right after finishing a major project will only stop you in your tracks. You'll need to make the space and build back your energy reserves before you transition to whatever comes next.

What Areas Need Attention?
Identify what areas of your life and work were impacted by the project and now need attention.

Environmental   Physical spaces, containers, tools, and materials used
during your project

Digital   Computers, tablets, phone, hard drives, memory
cards, cloud storage, apps

Social   Consider areas of your social life that may need tending
to after intense focus elsewhere

MAKE TIME FOR CAT WORK

The process of getting projects done is messy. Giving yourself CAT (clean up, archive, and trash) time will make the next project easier to do because you won't be fighting the messes of your last project. Make sure to schedule at least one focus block at the end of your project for CAT work.

Verb It! CAT work has its own verb list:

Clean Up
to make sense of what's around you and close loops:

Sort	Wipe	Plus social loop-closers like:
Categorize	Restock	Thank
Tag	Replace	Follow up
Tidy	Record	Check in
Maintain	Itemize	
Wash	Reconcile	

Archive
to make things easy to find in the future:

Store	Record	Index
File	Catalog	Scan
Label	Compress	Inventory
Organize	Zip	

Trash
to get rid of what you no longer need:

Recycle	Throw away	Let go
Donate	Delete	Dispose
	Remove	

MAKE YOUR NEXT PROJECT EASIER, BETTER, AND MORE FUN

Throughout the stages of getting the project done, you've had a lot of wins as well as varying degrees of setbacks and challenges, and you've figured out how to get and keep momentum. An **After-Action Review** (AAR) will make your project a learning experience while making your next project easier, better, and more fun.

The Five Questions of the AAR

1. What went well?	Consider all the people, processes, and tools that made the project go well.
2. What setbacks, challenges, or missteps did I experience?	Include challenges you had with other people, your planning, environment, or tools.
3. What did I learn?	Include project-specific lessons as well as those that might apply to all projects.
4. What habits, practices, or routines do I want to keep doing going forward?	You likely had to develop or reinforce some habits, practices, or routines. Note what worked.
5. Were there any especially important difference makers for this project?	List the top items (good and bad) that you'll want to remember in the future.

➕ You can find a link to the After-Action Review worksheet on the Resources page.

⬡ WHAT HAS COMPLETING YOUR PROJECT UNLOCKED?

Finishing a best-work project unlocks new realities. Take time to take stock of what this project has unlocked for you.

Has This Project Unlocked...

New Projects?	Did it inspire new ideas or simply open the space to move on new projects?	Add them to the culled down Project List you created in chapter 3.
GATES?	What are you better at than you were before?	Update your GATES list from chapter 6.
New Relationships or Communities?	Who has this project brought into your life?	Add them to your Network Scan from chapter 4.
Mindsets and Stories?	What stories have you proven true or untrue?	Update your No-Win Scenarios and Limiting Beliefs from chapter 7.
Portfolio Points?	Do you have something to add to your portfolio, resume, or vita?	Update your online profiles, website, resume, or share with your boss/HR.

Set goals, make plans, put the plans to work, and navigate the void to go from idea to done. Celebrate the victories you accrue and be proud of the work. But when your work is done, take a breather, set new sights, and start finishing anew.

Every best-work project you finish leaves more
of your fingerprints on the universe.

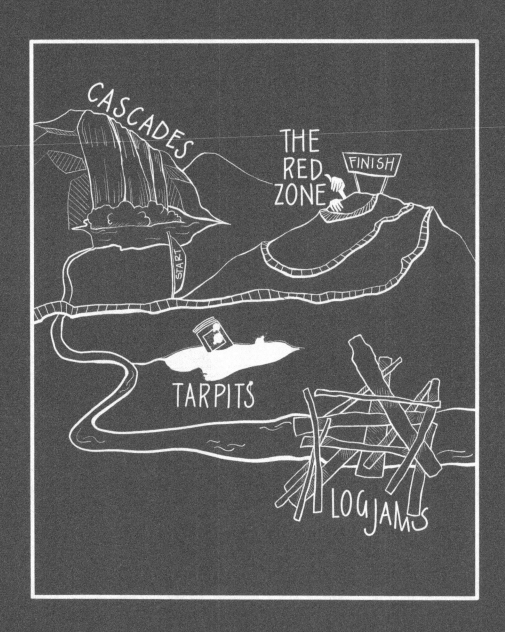

WHAT TO DO IF YOUR PROJECT GETS STUCK

In an ideal world, we'd build a perfect road map, our schedules would actually be what we'd planned they'd be, and there wouldn't be any disruptions to throw us off. But in the real world projects get off track, and the more a project gets off track, the more likely it is to end up stuck.

WHY ARE YOU STUCK?

First things first: you are not uniquely defective. Projects get stuck and projects fail. That's simply a fact of life in Project World. Usually this is an indication there is a misalignment somewhere.

- Did you say yes too quickly when you were already overcommitted?

- Did you charge ahead by yourself rather than asking for help?

- Did a streak of easy wins unlock a new level of challenge that you weren't ready for?

- Did your idea not match your actual priorities and the projects that relate to your priorities won out?

- Did you have an idea not a project (i.e., you didn't commit to a plan)?

- Did you get tripped up over the remnants of past projects that need to be cleaned up, archived, or trashed?

- Did you have the wrong people on your team for the wrong reasons?

- Did you need more time honing your skills or collecting your resources?

- Did you have a bad handoff to someone else and are waiting on feedback or approval before you can move forward?

- Did you have a beautiful plan that reality shattered in wonderful or terrible ways you couldn't anticipate?

Just as a project in motion tends to stay in motion, a project at rest tends to stay at rest.

HOW ARE YOU STUCK?

Projects slip and end up stuck for different reasons. Understanding how and why can help you get back on track or avert the issue entirely.

Identify the Stuck

Isolate the stuck project(s) in your mind, among all the other things that might be swirling. Which **one statement** best describes the situation you're facing?

I've gotten behind on one project, and it's making everything else fall behind causing a backlog of project tasks coming due faster than I can possibly address them.

→ Go to page 118 for steps you can take to slow the flow of the **Cascade** you're dealing with so you can come up for air.

I have multiple projects going on at the same time and I just don't have enough focus blocks to get them all done. Everything is at a standstill.

→ Go to page 119 for ways to clear out this **Logjam** and hopefully prevent a future cascade.

My project has been stuck for a long time and it's really difficult to figure out how to get it unstuck (or even if I should).

→ Go to page 120 for how to handle this project that has become stuck in a **Tarpit** before it gets stuck for good.

I'm close to the end of my project and things keep coming up (distractions, feelings, head trash, etc.) that are slowing me down and preventing me from finishing.

→ Go to page 121 for ways to manage your way through the **Creative Red Zone** and get your project across the finish line.

GET UNSTUCK

After you've determined what has you stuck, use the relevant checklists to guide you in getting your project unstuck from its cascade, logjam, or tarpit, or move you through your project's creative red zone.

How to Handle a Cascade

Cascade = when a delay on one project causes a backlog of project tasks coming due faster than you can possibly address them

You don't get out of a cascade by continuing to shuffle projects or by simply working faster; you get out of them by finishing the essential projects and committing to fewer projects once you're out of the cascade.

Step 1: Put all optional projects on hold.
"Optional" meaning anything that won't get you in hot water if not done. You can return to them once you're in calmer waters.

Step 2: Say no to new projects when you can.
New projects will only make a cascade harder to manage. You may need to make a case to any project delegators for a "new project timeout."

Step 3: Sort your remaining projects by importance.
Prioritize projects so you can determine which need to be worked on first. Use the snowball method until you get caught up.

Step 4: Work on projects sequentially.
Better to finish a project or two a week using the snowball method than to make a little progress on a handful of projects.

Step 5: Use the Five Projects Rule
Cascades often occur because we commit to too many projects in the first place.

How to Clear Out a Logjam

Logjam = when too many projects compete for your limited time and you're at a standstill

Dealing with a logjam once you're in it almost always amounts to triaging your project and punting subordinate or less-important projects into following weeks, which may result in a cascade that you'll then need to address. But the more projects that get crammed into the logjam, the harder it's going to be to get any of them unstuck.

Step 1: Review your conflicting projects.
Determine which projects are competing for the same limited focus blocks.

Step 2: Identify which chunks will get a project moving.
If one project starts to move, it tends to open up space for others to move as well.

Step 3: Triage your projects and renegotiate deadlines.
Assess priority and stagger projects so you don't have so many coming due at the same time and prevent future logjams.

Step 4: Anticipate and address logjams before they happen.
Be on the lookout for chunks of projects that are likely to cause snags and prioritize finishing them so your logjam doesn't turn into a cascade.

How to Extricate a Project Stuck in a Tarpit

Tarpit = when a project has been stuck for so long that it's difficult to figure out how to get it unstuck

The tarpit is different from cascades and logjams because, not only is the project stuck and sinking, but lightly pushing the project isn't going to get it going. You've got to figure out what else might be stuck to it and clean the muck off before you can get it back in "Active" projects without worrying that it'll start sinking again.

Step 1: Make sure the project isn't dead.
If it's dead, then let it go.

Step 2: If it's alive, reconnect with the pain of not doing it.
Which would cause you more pain: not getting your other projects done or not getting this one done? Pain can be a great motivator.

Step 3: Chunk the project into smaller pieces.
It will be easier to extract smaller pieces from a tarpit one at a time.

Step 4: Pick a chunk you can do within the next three days.
The goal is to get some movement since a project in motion is easier to keep in motion.

Step 5: Work on a project chunk at least twice a week.
This will prevent the project from sliding back into the tarpit.

Step 6: Avoid putting the project into a (metaphorical or literal) closet.
If you can't see the project, it's too easy for it to sink back into the tarpit.

How to Work Through the Creative Red Zone

Red Zone = when a project is close to the finish line and exhaustion and exasperation lead to overthinking and creative fatigue

While a red zone is not technically a stuck, your project can stall because of the inherent resistance (and its associated challenges) that crop up as you get closer to the finish line.

Step 1: Return to the why of the project.
When we shift to the hows and whens of a project, it's easy to lose sight of why we started in the first place.

Step 2: Focus on getting it to "good enough."
Perfection is unattainable so if that's your goal you'll never be done.

Step 3: Know the more it matters, the more it's only a start.
Your best work project is a building block to something bigger. So remember that the more something matters, the better it is that we start finishing sooner.

Step 4: Work on your own mindset.
Remember not to focus on what your naysayers and critics might say but on how your best work serves your beneficiaries.

Step 5: Do your work, step away.
The certainty of the outcome is out of your hands, so focus on doing the work while you're in it, and step away when you're done.

KEEP FUTURE PROJECTS FROM GETTING STUCK

By using the tools and ideas provided in this field guide, you can limit the points of stuckage and finally start finishing what matters most.

From Chapter 1   What does **Best Work** mean to you?

From Chapter 2   Which of the **Five Challenges** are most likely to get in the way of your success?

Which of the **Five Keys** need more practice?

From Chapter 3   Do you need to clean up your project list and **Pick a Project** that matters to you?

From Chapter 4   Have you reviewed the commitments and success strategies listed on your **Project Scoper?**

Who on your **Success Pack** can you reach out to for help?

From Chapter 5   Do you need to break your project down into smaller **Chunks?**

Have you scheduled enough focus blocks on your **Weekly Block Scheduler?**

From Chapter 6	How can you use your **GATES?**
	Did you allocate enough of a **Project Budget?**
	Have you mapped out your **12-week Project Roadmap?**
From Chapter 7	Have you conducted a **Project Pre-Mortem** to identify the drag points that can lead to a stuck?
From Chapter 8	Are you using the **5/10/15 Split** to build daily momentum and identify potential points of stuckage?
From Chapter 9	Are your **Habits and Routines** helping or hindering you?
From Chapter 10	Do you need to do some **CAT Work** to prevent current projects getting stuck in the detritus of past projects?
	How will you use the learnings from your **AARs** to inform future planning?

All of the resources referenced in this field guide (and more!) are available at

productiveflourishing.com/start-finishing/ resources/

Days spent doing your best work compound
to create a thriving life.

CPSIA information can be obtained
at www.ICGtesting.com
Printed in the USA
BVHW011338180422
634463BV00002B/9

9 798985 441604